★　　★　　★　　★　　★

THE CHEERLEADERS ALMANAC

★　　★　　★　　★　　★

By K. D. Kuch

Illustrated by J. J. Smith-Moore

Endorsed by the
National Cheerleaders Association

D0172559

Bullseye Books
Random House 🏠 New York

*Many thanks to the advisers and cheerleaders who took the time
to talk with me. I've learned so much.*

—K. D. K.

A Bullseye Book published by Random House, Inc.

Copyright © 1996 by RGA Publishing Group, Inc.

All rights reserved under International and Pan-American Copyright Conventions.
Published in the United States by Random House, Inc., New York, and simultaneously in
Canada by Random House of Canada Limited, Toronto.

Library of Congress Cataloging-in-Publication Data:

Kuch, K. D.

The cheerleaders almanac / by K. D. Kuch; illustrated by J. J. Smith-Moore.

    p. cm.

SUMMARY: Explains how to survive cheerleading tryouts and perform amazing stunts.
Includes information on the latest trends and quotes from cheerleaders across the
country.

ISBN: 0-679-87763-0 (pbk.)

1. Cheerleading—Juvenile literature. [1. Cheerleading.] I. Smith-Moore, J. J., 1955– ill.
II. Title. LB3635.K83 1996

791.6'4—dc20

95-36533

Manufactured in the United States of America 10 9 8 7 6 5 4 3 2 1

CONTENTS

★ ★ ★ ★ ★

READY? . . . OKAY!

Your best friend does it. Your mom did it back when she was in school. Even your little brother's baby-sitter wants to do it. As a matter of fact, millions of kids are doing it all over the country! What is it? Cheerleading! And it's one of the fastest-growing activities among school-age kids in the United States today.

You'll find cheerleaders on the athletic fields and courts at colleges, high schools and junior high schools, even elementary schools. They're cheering through local youth leagues and for all-star squads, which are set up just for cheerleading competitions. In the past five years, cheerleading has become so popular worldwide that squads have started up in Japan, Canada, and Europe. Most professional football and basketball teams have their own cheerleaders. Who hasn't seen (or heard) the football-cheering Dallas Cowboys Cheerleaders or the basketball-supporting L.A. Laker Girls? Some of these cheerleaders even have fans of their own!

There's something special about these high-spirited leaders. Their athletic good looks, endless enthusiasm, and ear-to-ear smiles make them stand out in any crowd, and their riveting cheers make them well heard, too!

4

CHEERLEADER STATS

Who are cheerleaders? Take a look at the latest statistics from the National Cheerleaders Coaches Conference:

Teens: 81% are ages 14 to 18

16% are ages 11 to 13

Leaders: 83% are leaders in student organizations

Athletes: 62% are involved in a second sport

Academics: 83% carry a B average or better

So you want to know more, right? You have questions—like, how do I get started? Are tryouts really hard? What do I wear when I cheer? How does my squad raise money for uniforms? Are there camps or clinics where I can train? What's it *really* like to be a cheerleader?

Sit tight—because this book has all of these answers, and more! So start reading . . . and soon you'll be ready . . . Okay!

SO *THIS* IS CHEERLEADING!

You've seen them jumping up and down on the sidelines, yelling for your favorite team. That doesn't seem so hard. So now you're wondering, "What does a cheerleader really do?" There's a whole lot more to cheerleading than jumping around entertaining a crowd.

★ ***On the sidelines, cheerleaders support the school's athletic teams.*** Working as a squad, they create and perform exciting chants and cheer routines to encourage fans to get behind the team. Team members will try harder if they know their fans support them. Think of a cheerleading squad as the bridge between the crowd and the team.

★ ***Off the sidelines, cheerleaders represent the school and promote school spirit year-round.*** Cheerleaders always have to be ready to project enthusiasm, sportsmanship, and teamwork. They're like goodwill ambassadors spreading positive word about your school.

ON BEING A CHEERLEADER

There are as many reasons to cheer as there are cheerleaders. It's a great athletic activity. For some people it's a competitive outlet. As a cheerleader you get to entertain crowds of people. And it's a cool way to help build school spirit and enthusiasm.

"Being a cheerleader was a dream I had ever since I was a little girl. I went to every football game I could and every basketball game and watched the cheerleaders. Then I'd practice on my own. I love being in front of the crowd cheering my team on!"
— VERONICA C., CLINTON HIGH SCHOOL, CLINTON, MISSOURI

"I got into cheering because all my friends were doing it. It was something that brought us all together in middle school. A lot of them went away, but I kept on doing it. I guess I'm hooked. This is my eighth season as a cheerleader and I can't get enough of it."
— KATIE R., NEWBURYPORT HIGH SCHOOL, NEWBURYPORT, MASSACHUSETTS

"I really like doing stunts, and I like being in front of a crowd. When you walk off the field or court happy, you know you've done a good job."
— WHITNEY W., MARATHON HIGH SCHOOL, MARATHON, FLORIDA

"Once, our football coach told us that during a couple of the games he was really mad at some of his players, but he said hearing us cheer made him feel better. It's a lot of fun to hear that."
— TRACI D., HEPPNER HIGH SCHOOL, HEPPNER, OREGON

LET'S START AT THE BEGINNING

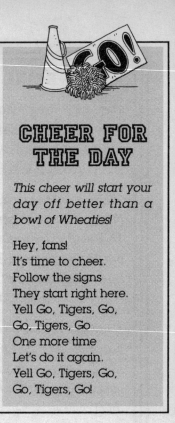

There's no real record of when and where organized cheerleading began, but cheering for a favorite person or group seems to be an instinctive part of human nature. It's only been in the last fifty years or so that cheerleading has developed into the activity that we recognize today. In the early days of college cheerleading, cheers were led by guys, while girls performed pom pon routines to music during halftimes. Then someone realized girls were easier to lift and use in the elaborate stunts and pyramids that wowed the crowds. Before long, girls were standing shoulder-to-shoulder with the male cheerleaders. Today, female cheerleaders outnumber guys 20 to 1 on most high school squads. And what was cheerleading like before organized cheers, all-girl squads, and pom pons?

CHEER FOR THE DAY

This cheer will start your day off better than a bowl of Wheaties!

Hey, fans!
It's time to cheer.
Follow the signs
They start right here.
Yell Go, Tigers, Go,
Go, Tigers, Go
One more time
Let's do it again.
Yell Go, Tigers, Go,
Go, Tigers, Go!

Ancient Times

Spectators cheered for runners at footraces held during the first Olympic Games in ancient Greece.

Great Britain, 1860s

Students at schools in Great Britain began spontaneously cheering at competitive sporting events. Soon the idea of cheering spread to America.

Princeton, New Jersey, 1865

Male students and team supporters formed the first pep club and created the first-known cheer:

> Tah rah rah
> Tiger Tiger Tiger
> Sis sis sis
> Boom boom boom
> Aaaahhhhh!
> Princeton! Princeton! Princeton!

Minneapolis, Minnesota, 1898

The first official cheerleader made *his* debut at the University of Minnesota. Student Johnny Campbell was elected "yell marshal," and he started leading his fellow fans in cheers at the U of M football games.

Dallas, Texas, 1948

Former gymnast and cheerleader Lawrence Herkimer first put together workshops to train cheerleaders. Those workshops gave birth to the National Cheerleaders Association (NCA), the first and one of the most established groups dedicated to training cheerleaders. NCA is the largest privately held cheerleading company in the world. (Herkimer invented both the Herkie jump and the pom pon.)

United States, 1950s

Cheerleading reached the height of popularity (matched only by today's reception) and girls began outnumbering guys on the sidelines.

RAH RAH!

When Johnny Campbell delivered his first cheer, there were no cheerleading uniforms, no pom pons or megaphones. (But it's thought that he did use a cowbell to pump up the crowds.) With or without props, Johnny managed to motivate the University of Minnesota football fans and start the cheerleader tradition with this yell:

Rah rah rah!
Sku-u-mah, hoo-rah!
Hoo-rah!
Varsity! Varsity!
Minn-e-so-tah!

IN GOOD COMPANY

Cheerleading has experienced amazing growth since its start in the United States. Organizations like the National Cheerleaders Association provide information to schools and cheer squads and hold cheer camps around the country. Primarily dedicated to junior high, high school, and college cheerleaders, they also sponsor national competitions that are seen on television by millions of people. And they give cheerleaders the opportunity to participate in special events, such as cheering at bowl games and parades all around the globe.

The fastest-growing segment of cheerleading is happening in youth leagues, sponsored by such organizations as the YMCA. Cheer groups for youngsters, ages seven to thirteen, are popping up all over. Even Pop

Warner Football, an organization that promotes youth football, has started sponsoring cheer squads. Local parks and recreation departments also provide programs.

These junior cheer groups teach cheerleading basics. But don't be fooled—just because it's called a youth league doesn't mean they're teaching kid stuff! These young cheerleaders are learning the latest cheers, chants, and jumps—the same material being performed by cheerleaders on top high school and college squads.

Want to find out more about youth leagues in your area? Try contacting your local parks and recreation department.

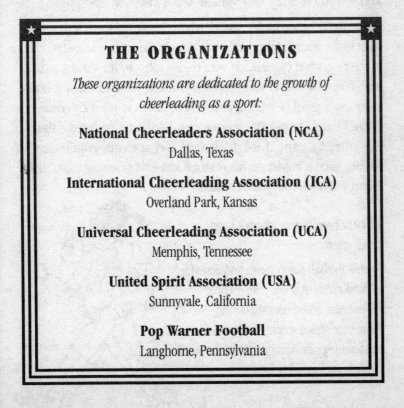

THE ORGANIZATIONS

These organizations are dedicated to the growth of cheerleading as a sport:

National Cheerleaders Association (NCA)
Dallas, Texas

International Cheerleading Association (ICA)
Overland Park, Kansas

Universal Cheerleading Association (UCA)
Memphis, Tennessee

United Spirit Association (USA)
Sunnyvale, California

Pop Warner Football
Langhorne, Pennsylvania

SOMETHING TO SHOUT ABOUT

Imagine an athlete who practices many hours each week, works hard to help the team win its competitions, and can still carry a 3.5 grade point average. Does a cheerleader come to mind? It should. But to a lot of people that isn't the case. More than any other athlete, the typical high school cheerleader has often received a bum rap. Here are a few of the myths that have circulated countless school halls—and the straight facts behind them!

Myth: If you're pretty and popular, you'll make the cheer squad.

Fact: Today's cheerleader cannot rely on looks to earn a spot on the spirit leader team. It takes hard work to make the squad and to stay on it. In the past, when cheerleaders were elected solely by the student body, it *was* more of a beauty and popularity contest. However, many schools today use a panel of trained, independent judges to select cheerleaders. "Beauty" and "popularity" are not even listed on judges' score sheets. The criteria consist of tough physical and academic requirements. Looking good is important, but neatness and good grooming count more than if you're wearing gobs of makeup.

Myth: Cheerleading doesn't take much effort.

Fact: A football player trains and plays for a few months out of the year. A cheerleader trains and cheers almost the entire year. After a summer of practice and learning new routines, a squad cheers through the football season, the

basketball season, and the volleyball or wrestling season. Then cheerleaders have their own cheerleading competitions to prepare for.

And when the cheerleaders aren't performing on the sidelines, they're the biggest promoters of school spirit within the halls, hanging up posters and organizing pep rallies (that's a school assembly to build up school spirit before a game). They also put on fund-raising events to pay for their uniforms, summer camp trips, and other supplies.

SECRET OF MY SUCCESS

"I started gymnastics when I was five years old and I would recommend it if you are planning to be a cheerleader."

MANDY H.,
BARREN COUNTY HIGH SCHOOL,
GLASGOW, KENTUCKY

Myth: *Anyone can be a cheerleader. It's not like a* real *sport.*

Fact: Cheerleading involves the most difficult elements of several sports and performance arts. It requires the skill of a gymnast, the endurance of a long-distance runner, and the grace and timing of a dancer.

It takes the same commitment to be a good cheerleader, as it does to be an athlete. Most squads practice at least two hours a day, three to four times a week. Besides games, some cheering squads take part in cheerleading competitions. Many of these are put on by the national cheerleading organizations. A few states—Michigan, West Virginia, Virginia, Maine, Georgia, Vermont, and Florida—have recognized cheering as part of school sports. These states have specific guidelines for cheerleading, just as they do for their high school sports. (And they hold their own cheerleading tournaments.)

ON STEREOTYPES

"I really hate those cheerleader stereotypes—you know, fluff-chicks."
—JENNY P., WALSH JESUIT HIGH SCHOOL, CUYAHOGA FALLS, OHIO

"Those stereotypes are very, very wrong. We have class presidents on our squads. We have people who carry 4.0 grade points. We have a lot of talented, smart people."
—MARIBEL C., BANNING HIGH SCHOOL, WILMINGTON, CALIFORNIA

"I'd always heard the stereotypes about cheerleaders. They don't have any brains. They don't have to be athletes. Now that I'm the school mascot and I work out with the cheerleaders, I've seen for myself that's not true. The truth just shatters all those old stereotypes."
—STEVE S., SHERANDO HIGH SCHOOL, STEPHENS CITY, VIRGINIA

DO YOU HAVE WHAT IT TAKES?

No two cheerleaders are alike and no two schools have exactly the same requirements for their cheerleaders. But experts usually agree that the following characteristics are very beneficial, if not mandatory, to be an effective cheerleader.

Stamina

Cheerleading takes a lot of energy, and like that little pink rabbit, you must keep going and going and going. Practices, games, and competitions take endurance and good physical conditioning. One way to increase your stamina is with aerobic activity. Running and aerobics classes are good ways to build up your stamina. Do it on your own or with friends, or check out your local YMCA for classes.

Coordination

A good sense of rhythm and the ability to keep in step with other squad members is a must. Turn on your CD player, put on your favorite tunes, and start dancing. If you want formal training, look in the Yellow Pages for dance classes.

Gymnastic Skills

Tumbling has become a more significant part in cheerleading. Cheerleaders cartwheel onto the field and use gymnastic skills in their stunts and pyramids. Check with your phys. ed. instructor for suggestions on where to get extra help.

Flexibility

Sometimes it looks as if cheerleaders have Silly Putty for bones. They bend this way or that. There's no question that being flexible and limber will allow you to perform all your movements, especially jumps, without injury. The best way to increase your flexibility is with stretching exercises, such as those found on pages 41 and 42.

Good Voice Quality

If you're watching a game from the bleachers, you don't want to have to strain to hear what the cheerleaders are yelling. Your voice is the tool you use to get your message across. Your voice must be strong to be heard in the stands, and you need to place the proper accent on words and say the cheers clearly enough to be easily understood.

Enthusiasm

An energetic personality is necessary to lead and charm a crowd every week. One of the most effective ways to show your genuine enthusiasm is with a wide, sincere smile. (No fake grins allowed!)

Good Health

It's important to maintain a weight that's healthy for your height and age. Develop good eating habits and stick to foods that provide important vitamins and nutrients. If you need to lose weight, don't try any crash diets. All they do is rob you of valuable energy. Always check with a doctor before starting any weight-loss plan.

School Performance

Almost all squads require good grades. That might be a 2.5 grade point average or better. Some schools require teacher recommendations before you can even try out.

A Team Player

A cheerleading squad is made up of individuals who must work as a team. While the members of a squad don't have to be best friends, everyone should want the same goal . . . to make the squad the best it can be. Squads usually vote on all important matters, from selecting cheers to picking out uniforms. The best squads also have open discussions in which members can voice their concerns and frustrations.

RULES TO CHEER BY

You've probably read the United States Constitution in history class. Did you know that your school has a cheerleaders' constitution? The constitution covers everything a cheerleader needs to know, from requirements for trying out to a code of ethics. A copy of your school's cheerleading constitution should be available at tryout practice. Pretend it's another history assignment—and memorize it!

The Cheerleader's Constitution

Here's a sample constitution taken from the *NCA 1995 Official Advisor/Coach Handbook*. It may not be exactly like your school's, but it will give you an idea of the time and commitment that it takes to become a cheerleader.

I. PURPOSE
   A. A cheerleader shall promote school spirit and develop good sportsmanship among the student body and better relations between schools in the conference.

II. THE SQUADS
   A. There shall be one varsity squad composed of ____ *(varies according to school)* students who are juniors and seniors.
   B. There shall be one junior varsity squad composed of ____ *(varies according to school)* freshmen and sophomores.
   C. Each squad will have a head cheerleader/captain selected by squad mates and approved by adviser, and also a co-head cheerleader/co-captain. Both will be responsible for leading and guiding the squad in accordance with its purpose.

III. UNIFORMS
   A. Cheerleaders are responsible for uniform costs that exceed money allotted by the School Board.

B. Prior to being ordered, uniforms must be approved by the adviser.

C. Uniforms are to be cleaned after each game, as are cheering shoes.

D. Uniforms are to be worn only for games and rallies, unless permission is granted by the adviser.

IV. GAMES

A. Cheerleaders must attend ALL home and away football and basketball games.

B. Cheerleaders must arrive at least thirty minutes before each game.

V. TRANSPORTATION

A. Cheerleaders must travel to and from away games in transportation provided by the school.

B. Permission to travel with parents must be accompanied by a note from a parent and approved by adviser.

VI. PRACTICES

A. Attendance at practice is required.

B. It is each cheerleader's responsibility to be ready by the time practice begins.

VII. CONDUCT

A. Cheerleaders should conduct themselves as official student representatives of the school.

B. They should not smoke, drink alcoholic beverages, or use profanity while in uniform.

C. They should act in a sportsmanlike manner at all times and discourage any unsportsmanlike conduct of supporters.

D. Cheerleaders should willingly cooperate with the head cheerleader, squad mates, adviser, coaches, and the administration.

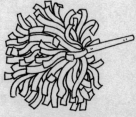

VIII. REQUIREMENTS

A. To remain eligible to cheer, cheerleaders must maintain at least a ____ average *(varies according to school)* in each subject and satisfactory citizenship grades.

B. All cheerleaders must attend summer camp with the squad.

C. All cheerleaders are required to have a physical examination prior to camp.

IX. DISMISSAL

A. A cheerleader shall be dismissed for smoking or drinking alcoholic beverages in uniform.

B. A cheerleader may be dismissed for unbecoming conduct that reflects poorly on the school.

C. If scholastic average falls below a ____ average *(varies according to school)* for two grading periods, dismissal from the squad will result.

D. A cheerleader will also be dismissed if he or she accumulates ____ demerits *(varies according to school)*.

X. TRYOUT PROCEDURE

A. A two-week training program *(varies according to school)* will be conducted by current cheerleaders one month prior to tryouts.

B. A screening committee—made up of the retiring head cheerleader, two cheerleader instructors from a recognized cheerleader association, two cheerleaders from a nearby college or two cheerleader advisers from other schools *(varies according to school)*—will observe and judge the performances of all candidates and announce to the student body a list of the most qualified candidates.

C. All candidates will wear numbers to designate who they are when they try out. Required will be two cheers, three different jumps, and two partner stunts *(varies according to school)*.

THE CAPTAIN IS...

Being elected captain of your cheerleading squad is an exciting moment. Just imagine, your squad mates feel you have what it takes to lead them and keep them on track. Most squads elect one member to fill this important position. As captain, you'll work with the adviser, keep a notebook of activities and cheers, and mediate disputes between squad members.

Some schools are now advocating a "captain of the week" approach. Each week a different cheerleader is the squad captain. This avoids overloading one person with all the work and gives everyone a chance to participate.

LOOKING THE PART

When you think of a cheerleader's uniform, you usually think of a short skirt and sweater. Today, spirit leaders have a lot more fashion options. Most squads decide as a group what uniforms they will wear. Some squads have outfits for each sports season. Squad budgets will be a big factor in how many uniforms are allowed. National organizations like NCA also supply uniforms and equipment to cheerleaders. They have catalogs filled with the latest fashions.

Athletic wear companies are designing high-performance uniforms in comfortable, long-wearing, easy-care fabrics. Whatever the fabric, a uniform should always be cleaned and pressed immediately after a game.

Here's a list of uniform "must haves" that no nineties cheerleader should live without!

For the Girls

Skirt: Standard issue for most cheerleaders. These short (upper thigh) skirts come pleated or in yoke-front gathers. The newest design from NCA is the fly-away™ skirt. It's designed with split panels that twirl as you move. They're available in several solid colors or combinations. Most squads try to incorporate their school colors.

Shell: This sleeveless, cropped top matches the skirt to complete the cheerleader's uniform. Sleeveless tops are great for warm weather, or if you are cheering for an indoor sport—say, basketball. When it turns cold, some cheerleaders opt to wear turtlenecks underneath.

Sweater: Perfect for football season, these long-sleeved sweaters come in crew neck, turtleneck, and V neck options. And there's plenty of room for arm movements.

Jumper: This one-piece connects the skirt and top together. With lots of options available, you can choose from several top and bottom combinations. Do you want a V neck or a sweetheart neck? How about a pleated, yoke-front, or fly-away™ skirt? The appeal of a one-piece is its simplicity.

One-Piece Pants Outfit: Some squads are turning to the pants outfit. It usually consists of a one-piece bodysuit and a vest. This outfit is becoming popular with some squads who believe it accentuates their movements and gives them a more streamlined appearance during competitions.

Brief Trunks: Worn under the skirts, these briefs—or bloomers, as they are sometimes called—are color-coordinated to match the uniforms.

Sports Bra: Not a requirement, but some cheerleaders like the support a sports bra gives them.

For the Guys

Pants/Shorts: The guys wear pants and shorts that match the girls' skirts. The pants come in solid colors. Stripes down the sides can be added to match girls' skirts.

Shirts: These short-sleeved tops are designed to match the girls' uniforms.

Sweaters: Generally identical to their squad mates' sweaters, but cut to fit a guy.

For Everyone

Warm-up Suits: Worn usually when the squad travels, warm-up suits are designed to coordinate with the squad's uniforms.

Emblems or Letters: Emblem designs such as megaphones, stars, and animals (to match your school's mascot) are attached to your sweater or top. Often, the emblem will have the cheerleader's name sewn on it.

Shoes: Major athletic shoe manufacturers have started making shoes just for cheerleaders. They're lightweight and have extra support. Shoes can be ordered in specific colors to match uniforms. Some shoes contain pockets on the outside and inside of each shoe that come with several different colors of small plastic inserts. This allows the cheerleader to put in whatever color he or she wishes. There are even special shoes to wear for doing stunts. These have cushioned soles that won't dig into your stunt partner's shoulder and finger grooves for easier gripping.

Accessories: Socks, gloves (for cold weather cheering), tote bags, and hair bows to hold ponytails or braids are available to be matched to the uniforms.

ON UNIFORMS

"Our squad has three outfits: A pleated skirt with a shell top for day games, or if we're doing a parade. For the second outfit we wear the same skirt, but we wear it with a long-sleeved sweater. Then we have a sweatsuit outfit and a jacket to match."

—MERISSA B., BANNING HIGH SCHOOL, WILMINGTON, CALIFORNIA

"For my school squad we wear the traditional vest, turtleneck, and skirt. But for the all-star squad I'm on, we wear a one-piece outfit."

—JENNY P., WALSH JESUIT HIGH SCHOOL, CUYAHOGA FALLS, OHIO

TOOLS OF THE TRADE

Cheerleaders use more than spirited routines and rousing cheers to get a crowd excited—they also use props. These props can add visual excitement to a routine as well as help motivate crowds. Some common cheerleading tools are megaphones, signs, and pom pons, all of which can be found in cheerleaders' supply catalogs.

Megaphones

Megaphones amplify the sound and help spread it to more people in the crowd. When you use a megaphone, yell directly into it instead of holding it away from your mouth.

Signs

Signs are used to spell out words you want the crowd to yell back. Always show your audience the signs first, and let them know how they should respond. Make sure the signs are big enough for everyone to see, but not so big that you can't handle them. The best size is about 3' by 3'. You can also get a whole section of spectators even more involved by passing out signs that *they* hold up for the sports team to see at a crucial moment in a game.

Pom Pons

Poms make the cheerleaders look more visual and add flash. When using poms during a routine, your motions need to be sharp and clean. Poms today are small fluffy balls of plastic streamers, usually in your school colors. Standard sizes can be ordered, from 6" to 13" (the length of the streamers).

GET CREATIVE!

USE A MEGAPHONE AS A SIGN

Cover the side of the megaphone with paper to spell out words or slogans, like GO FIGHT WIN or T-I-G-E-R-S. Don't forget to add your team's name to the side of the megaphone. Point to it when you want the crowd to yell out the team's name!

CUE THE CROWD WITH POMS

Use pom pons to cue the crowd when you want the crowd to yell back. It works really well for yelling back the school colors. If you want the crowd to yell "Red," hold up the red pom. When you want them to yell "Blue," hold up the blue pom.

COUNTDOWN TO TRYOUTS

You've made the decision. You're going to do it. You're going to try out for the cheerleading squad. So now what?

Cheerleading tryout programs often vary from school to school. But there are some common practices that will help you prepare for those nerve-racking tryouts. Just watch—with each passing week of preparations, those butterflies will be flying away!

IMMEDIATELY

Meet the cheerleading adviser.

If you don't already know who this is, check with the school office. Find out from the adviser when tryouts will be held. It'll probably be in the spring. That gives the new squad time to practice together and attend cheerleading camp during the summer.

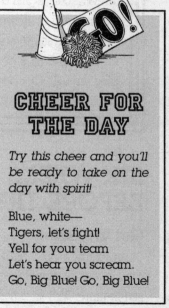

CHEER FOR THE DAY

Try this cheer and you'll be ready to take on the day with spirit!

Blue, white—
Tigers, let's fight!
Yell for your team
Let's hear you scream.
Go, Big Blue! Go, Big Blue!

Flex now!

If you're not already doing it, start a program right now to stretch your muscles and increase your flexibility. You'll find stretching exercises on pages 41 and 42. Make it a daily ritual.

WHAT'S AN ADVISER?

Another name your adviser might go by is "coach." Your cheerleading adviser is probably a member of your school's faculty or staff. The adviser is someone who directs the practice sessions, prepares the squad for performances, and instructs and develops routines and cheers. The adviser is also responsible for uniforms and equipment. At the high school level and younger, the adviser is sometimes an unpaid volunteer or teacher who is willing to give up a lot of free time. Your adviser has probably gone through some sort of state-certified safety training, just like any of the coaches for other sports.

SIX WEEKS (OR MORE) BEFORE TRYOUTS

Get in shape!

Cheerleading is as strenuous as playing football or basketball. A combination of stamina, endurance, and flexibility will improve your performance. Well-stretched muscles will increase the height of your kicks and jumps. If you're not already in good shape, now is the time to do something about it. Running, swimming, and biking are excellent activities for overall aerobic conditioning.

Check out the current cheerleaders.

Often each cheer squad will have its own individual style. Some may be into hip-hop movements, while other squads stick to the traditional straight, sharp motions. If your school's squad uses a lot of gymnastic and dance movements, figure that you will, too. Don't be afraid to seek out help where needed. Maybe that means asking your school's phys. ed. teacher for help. Or you may want to take a few dance lessons to help with your coordination and rhythm.

TIPS FROM THE COACH

If you haven't been in a regular exercise program, expect some sore muscles. Don't try to pack all your conditioning into one giant workout session. Be consistent and try to work out three times a week for a minimum of half an hour each day.

FOUR WEEKS BEFORE TRYOUTS

Attend the pre-tryout meeting.

Approximately four weeks before the actual tryouts, a meeting is held of future cheerleaders. The adviser will announce the dates and times of the tryout clinics, as well as the date of the actual tryouts. You'll get the rules and requirements cheerleaders must meet. Depending on your school, you may have to meet all or just some of the following:

1. ***You need to be in good physical condition.***
   A medical checkup from your doctor is required before you can go to your first tryout practice.

2. *You may be required to have a minimum grade point average.* In most cases it's a 2.5 or better.

3. *You should be a good role model and school leader.* Are you involved in clubs, student government, or other school activities? Some schools require teachers' evaluations.

4. *You may be asked to write a brief essay to explain the importance of being a member of the cheerleading squad and the contributions you can make.* This will show your attitude toward teamwork and your dedication to the school and squad. It always helps to run your writing by a couple of friends or a parent to get their feedback. Your essay should be clear, concise, and fun to read.

5. *You'll also be asked to turn in a parental permission form.* Some schools may also want you and your parents to sign a Student Statement of Responsibility. Cheerleading is a demanding activity, and both you and your parents should read the form and understand the commitment you'll be taking on.

SECRET OF MY SUCCESS

"When trying out, all you should do is worry about yourself and not who is going to score higher than you."

CASIE M.,
CARL ALBERT JR. HIGH SCHOOL,
MIDWEST CITY, OKLAHOMA

Participate in the demonstration.

The current cheerleaders will show you some general jumps and gymnastics movements. They'll also perform the mandatory cheers and routines you will be judged on. Each school's requirements vary, but here are five categories often used in judging.

★ *A **Spirited Entrance*** to show you can grab a crowd's attention.

★ ***One Chant*** from two or three you'll be taught.

★ ***One Cheer*** that you're taught, or that you make up yourself to display your creativity.

★ ***Basic Cheerleading Skills***, including jumps, kicks, gymnastic stunts, and splits.

★ ***Lead a Group*** in cheers and chants to exhibit your leadership abilities, confidence, poise, and enthusiasm.

THREE WEEKS BEFORE TRYOUTS

Get organized.

Now that you know what's expected for tryouts, it's time to get to work on specifics and problem areas. Try some of these ideas to get ready:

1. ***Set up a practice schedule.*** Plan to practice one to two hours a day. If that sounds like a lot, remember that once you make the squad you'll be practicing around six hours a week, plus the games.

2. *Write it down.* It's one thing to say you're going to practice, it's another to do it. Create a daily planner with all your obligations (school, homework, baby-sitting jobs, doctors' appointments, and so on) blocked in. Then mark off your practice schedule. Highlight it with a bright colored marker. Be committed to your schedule.

3. *Make a list.* Take another piece of paper and write down your strong and weak points in cheering. Do you know the cheers by heart, but your jumps are less than perfect? Sometimes it's easy to practice those things you are already awesome at, while shoving aside those areas—maybe high kicks and toe-touch jumps?— that are more difficult. Be honest with yourself, and do extra work on your weak areas.

4. *Give yourself some free time.* Now, after saying how important it is to be committed to practicing, it is also vital that you don't overdo it. Take time to relax. Remember to schedule in a little fun time with friends.

Practice, Practice, Practice!

1. *Practice in front of a mirror.* You'll be able to see if you're doing the cheers right. Check how you look from different angles.

2. *Practice with a friend.* Even if your friend isn't trying out for a cheerleader spot, you still need her support and ideas. Tell your friend to be honest. It's great to hear

"You were perfect," but only if it's true. Be open to suggestions.

3. ***Practice yelling your cheers.*** Do the cheers as you will in tryouts—loud and clear. Since you may not be able to do this in front of a mirror or in your favorite practice room in the house, you may need to schedule a separate time just to practice yelling in an open area (your backyard or a park). To test how clear and loud your words are, put a tape recorder at the far side of the yard. Push the RECORD button and run about ten yards away. Practice your cheer. When you're finished, play back the tape. Can you hear yourself? Are your words clear?

4. ***Practice your smile.*** Okay, you might feel a little dorky standing in front of a mirror and just smiling—but you've got to get used to it! Does it look natural? You need to smile all the time, but you don't want it to look phony. Try using a little petroleum jelly on your upper gums. It helps keep your lips from drying out and sticking to your teeth. It may sound a little gross, but it works!

TIPS FROM THE COACH

Try to practice on the court or field where tryouts will be held (after you get the school's permission). Become familiar with the performance floor and surroundings, so you'll feel more comfortable during the actual tryout.

Hair and What to Wear

Deciding what to wear for practice sessions and tryouts won't be hard if you follow these suggestions:

1. **T-Shirt and Shorts:** Make them comfortable but nice-looking. Leave your grungies at home. Show school spirit by incorporating your school colors into your outfit.

2. **Shoes:** All you need for now is a good pair of athletic shoes with good support for jumping. Save the expensive cheerleader shoes for when you make the squad.

3. **Underwear:** If needed, get yourself a good, well-fitting sports bra.

4. **Hair:** Keep it out of your eyes. If you have long hair, use barrettes or pull your hair into a ponytail.

5. **Makeup:** Minimal! Go natural. All you probably need is a little lip gloss.

6. **Jewelry:** None! Watches, big earrings, necklaces, and scarves can be dangerous. Just think what snagging an earring can do to your earlobe!

ONE WEEK BEFORE TRYOUTS

Make it to the tryout clinics.

They're usually held during the week before the tryout. Some schools' clinics last only a day or two. Others hold the clinics for the entire week before the actual tryouts. Large schools hold first-round tryouts to eliminate candidates before the *final* tryout.

Ask for help.

The adviser and current cheerleaders will be at the clinic to help you. This is where you really get to work on your mandatory cheers and routines. If you have any questions about the execution of a cheer or jump, ask now! This will be your last chance before the tryout.

SECRET OF MY SUCCESS

"Judges always like the clean-cut appearance. Your hair should be tightly pulled back, your shirt should be tucked in, and you shouldn't wear too much makeup."

JENNY P.,
THOUSAND OAKS HIGH SCHOOL,
THOUSAND OAKS, CALIFORNIA

Pay attention to the judging information.

Every school has its own method for judging. There may be as many as four or five judges. They might include the cheerleading adviser and other faculty members, former cheerleaders, or out-of-town judges and coaches. The sample NCA judging score sheet on page 39 will give you an idea of what the judges look for.

Get enough sleep.

Getting sleep all week—not just the night before—is important. Without it, you can end up sluggish and not pumped up to your best potential.

THE NIGHT BEFORE TRYOUTS

Eat right.

When you're nervous, you may want to head for the fridge to eat a pint of ice cream. Or you may react the other way and live only on water. It's very important for you to eat a good dinner so you'll have energy the next day. If you overeat, you may feel tired. If you don't eat, you'll have no energy. You need more than butterflies in your belly! A meal of pasta (light on the sauce) and lots of salad will give you energy without making you feel huge!

Pack your bag.

You'll have a lot on your mind in the morning, so pack a bag tonight. Here's a checklist to make sure you don't forget anything:

- ❑ T-shirt and shorts
- ❑ Shoes and socks
- ❑ A hairbrush and hair spray
- ❑ Extra barrettes, combs, ribbons, rubber bands, bobby pins
- ❑ Deodorant
- ❑ Lip gloss, petroleum jelly, and hand lotion
- ❑ Safety pins (you never know when a bra strap might break)
- ❑ A towel

Pamper yourself.

You're going to be excited and your cheers will be running through your head a mile a minute. Relax! Turn on your favorite tunes and spoil yourself with a warm bubble bath.

TRYOUT DAY

Ease your fears.

Sweaty palms? Legs like Jell-O? Don't worry! It's probably just a bad case of nerves. Here are some suggestions to help calm the jitters.

★ First, being prepared should take some of the pressure away. If you've been practicing and rehearsing, you will have nothing to fear.

★ Take a deep breath, then release it. Empty those lungs! Let all those negative, anxious feelings blow out with the breath.

★ Close your eyes and see yourself performing your routine. Athletes do it all the time. It's called "visualization." Hear yourself chanting and cheering, and see the judges oohing and aahing over your perfect toe-touch jump.

It's over!

Congratulate yourself when you finish. You've planned, practiced, and worked hard to get through your first cheerleading tryout. Take some time to enjoy that fact.

AFTER TRYOUTS

Be patient.

Even one hour seems like one year when you're waiting. It might take a day or two for the judges to make their choices. The judges will rate you on your skill and performance, but your grades and teachers' evaluations may also be a factor. Keep your eyes open for a posting on the school bulletin board.

TIPS FROM THE COACH

During tryouts, if you make a mistake, just smile, compose yourself, and begin again. The judges will accept mistakes. What they want to see is how you recover from them.

If you made it . . .

Enjoy your moment of glory for a while—then it's back to work!

Get ready to try again.

If you didn't make the squad, be determined to try again next year. Get a copy of your score sheet. Use the judges' evaluations to see what you need to work on. You have a whole year to work to get ready! Remember, activities like gymnastics, dance, and aerobics can help improve your cheerleading skills.

OTHER WAYS TO SUPPORT YOUR SCHOOL

So you think shouting, jumping, and cartwheeling across the field are the only ways to cheer your favorite team to victory? Not so. Can you twirl a baton? Play an instrument? March to a drumbeat? Psych up a crowd? If you answered "yes" to any of these questions, then there's a place for you. Discover how you can be a spirit supporter on and off the field. Then check with your school office for the name of the adviser for each of these activities.

Pom Pons/Songleaders/ Dance Squad/Drill Team

They jump, leap, march, and rock the sidelines at halftime, but you won't hear one word from these spirit supporters. The pom/dance squad performs choreographed and complex dance routines, sometimes using pom pons. The drill team performs precision marching routines, using hand-held or larger props. These props can be flags, rifles, or banners. Other names you might hear this squad called are "pom squad," "dance team," or "pep squad."

Marching Band

The stadium rocks to their sound as the marching band tromps across the field. Dressed in uniforms with shiny brass buttons, sashes, and high-crowned hats called "busbies," the marching band performs at pre-game and halftime shows to keep the home crowd revved up.

Mascots

The mascot is usually a person, animal, or object adopted by the school to bring good luck to the home team. At games and for special activities like pep rallies, someone will dress as the mascot. Most schools hold a mascot tryout and pick one person for the position.

Pep Club

The pep club is made up of the various spirit groups within the school, including cheerleaders, songleaders, and members of the drill team. They're usually responsible for putting together the pep rallies. A pep rally is a chance to get the entire school excited about the upcoming game. Besides making signs, members of the pep club put on skits—short, funny plays that put everyone in the mood for a great game.

A MOST UNUSUAL MASCOT

These mascots are definitely one-of-a-kind!

Willy the Wave
Pepperdine University, Malibu, California

Zippy the Kangaroo
University of Akron, Akron, Ohio

Pete the Anteater
University of California at Irvine, Irvine, California

Pied Piper of Hamlin
Hamline University, St. Paul, Minnesota

Armadillo
Our Lady of the Lakes University, San Antonio, Texas

The most popular mascot is the eagle. Out of two thousand universities and colleges surveyed, seventy-two used the eagle as their mascot.

Twirlers

The baton whizzes overhead, then under a leg. It looks as if the twirler's hand is moving faster than the speed of light. Baton twirling takes a special talent, but it can be learned. And once you can twirl, there are all kinds of spirit supporting you can do. You could be a majorette, a person who leads the band onto the field and performs with them at halftime shows. A baton twirler uses a baton that is a metal shaft with round rubber balls on either end. A twirler can also twirl flags, fire batons, and sabers (swords).

NCA NATIONAL CHAMPIONSHIP OFFICIAL SCORESHEET

Squad Name _____ Division _____ Judge No. _____

CHEERLEADING FUNDAMENTALS	Max. Pts.	Execution	Degree of Difficulty
Motions	10		
Jumps	5 / 5		
Tumbling	5 / 5		
Partner Stunts/Pyramids	5 / 5		
Dance	5 / 5		

Strong Areas
- ❑ Good variety
- ❑ Sharp motions
- ❑ Good precision
- ❑ Good height
- ❑ Variety of jumps
- ❑ Good use of jumps
- ❑ Good variety of tumbling
- ❑ Good use of tumbling
- ❑ Good stunts
- ❑ Clean dismounts
- ❑ Good variety of stunts
- ❑ Music appropriate
- ❑ Good energy

Needs Improvement
- ❑ Not together
- ❑ Watch angles
- ❑ Need variety
- ❑ Needs to be stronger
- ❑ Point toes
- ❑ Work on height
- ❑ Add difficulty
- ❑ Not perfected
- ❑ No squad unity
- ❑ Dismounts shaky
- ❑ Stunts not strong
- ❑ Step, lock, tighten
- ❑ Add dance moves

ROUTINE EXECUTION	Max. Pts.	Points
PROJECTION		
Voice	5	
Expression/Showmanship	5	
CHOREOGRAPHY		
Timing	5	
Spacing/Formations	5	
Use of Floor	5	
Transitions/Flow	5	
Overall Crowd Appeal	5	
Creativity	5	
PERFECTION OF ROUTINE		
Performance Impression	10	

Strong Areas (Projection)
- ❑ Strong voices
- ❑ Good volume
- ❑ Good expression
- ❑ Genuine spirit
- ❑ Showy/spirited

Needs Improvement (Projection)
- ❑ Be louder
- ❑ Don't bark words
- ❑ Voices fade
- ❑ More smiles
- ❑ Energy level low
- ❑ Not together
- ❑ Too slow/Too fast
- ❑ Timing changed for building

Strong Areas (Choreography)
- ❑ Squad unity
- ❑ Good changes
- ❑ Good flow
- ❑ Good formation
- ❑ Smooth transitions
- ❑ Good use of squad-skills
- ❑ Good incorporation
- ❑ Good use of floor
- ❑ Good ideas
- ❑ Good variety

Needs Improvement (Choreography)
- ❑ Watch spacing
- ❑ Need changes/variety
- ❑ Break in routine flow
- ❑ Transition sloppy/choppy
- ❑ Add difficulty
- ❑ Stayed in same formation
- ❑ Same person in front
- ❑ Need variety
- ❑ Monotonous

Strong Areas (Perfection)
- ❑ Solid routine
- ❑ Clean routine

Needs Improvement (Perfection)
- ❑ Stunts off
- ❑ Some stunts late
- ❑ Falls
- ❑ Shaky - needs polish

TOTAL

General Comments:

ALL THE RIGHT MOVES

When you put a jigsaw puzzle together, you have to combine all the odd-shaped pieces to get the whole picture. Cheerleading is like that, too. There are lots of separate movements that have to be learned and then joined to make up a cheer. So get ready to learn the basics of stretching, jumps and stunts, cheer moves, and even YELLING!

STRE-E-E-ETCH THOSE MUSCLES!

Keeping your body stretched and limber is the most important thing a good cheerleader can do. Being flexible will protect against injuries, such as strains and muscle tears and soreness. Always start each practice session with exercises to warm up and stretch muscles. To really increase

CHEER FOR THE DAY

Here's a cheer to brighten anyone's day!

Get up, get up and go!
Go, Panthers, go!

40

your flexibility, do a series of stretching exercises, such as those below, every day to warm up your body from head to toe!

1. *Head Circles:* Slowly rotate your head forward, to the right, and to the left. Reverse direction. Do five times in each direction.

2. *Shoulder Rolls:* Relax your arms at your sides. Lift your shoulders upward and rotate them backward. Reverse direction. Do ten times in each direction.

3. *Arm Circles:* Stretch out your arms to your sides, holding them at shoulder level. Swing your arms forward in circular motions—start the circles small, gradually making them bigger. Now reverse direction, making your arms swing backward in circles. Repeat ten times in each direction.

4. *Waist Stretch:* Hold your arms out to your sides, parallel to the floor. Bend to the right and stretch your left arm over your head. Hold this position for thirty seconds. Now do it on the other side. Repeat this three times on each side.

5. *Hamstring Stretch:* With feet shoulder-width apart and your arms folded out in front of you, bend forward from the waist until you feel the tension in the back of your legs. Hold that position for thirty seconds and concentrate on relaxing your leg muscles. Return to an upright position and repeat the stretch, bending down toward your right leg and then toward the left leg. If you can, touch the floor with your fingertips. After stretching religiously for a while, you'll eventually be able to touch your palms to the floor! Repeat the entire sequence twice. You may need to bend your knees slightly at first to avoid injury!

6. *Runner's Stretch:* Lunge your right leg forward so that your knee is over your ankle. Your left leg should be straight behind you and your hands on the floor for balance. (You should feel an overall stretch in various areas of both legs.) Check the illustration to make sure you're in the right position. Hold for a count of 30, then press your left heel down into the floor for an extra stretch. Return to an upright position and change legs.

7. *Ankle Circles, Points, and Flexes:* While standing, raise your right foot a few inches off the floor and draw imaginary circles with your toes in an outward, then inward, direction. Repeat five times in each direction. Next point your foot to the floor, then flex it. Do each movement on each foot ten times.

HANDS, ARMS, AND FEET FIRST

When you watch a cheerleader, you'll notice that every part of the body is used. In competitions, judges will take off points if hand, arm, and leg movements are not performed just right. Here are some basic terms and positions to get you familiarized with a cheerleader's body lingo.

Basic Hand Positions

1. *Blades:* Hands are open with fingers closed together and thumb flat against the side of the index finger. Keep the wrist straight.

2. *Fists:* Curl fingers into a fist, with the thumb resting on the middle knuckle of the index and second fingers.

3. *Buckets:* Hands are in fists. Back of hand should be flat, not cocked up or down.

4. *Candlesticks:* Make a fist, curling the fingers lightly against the palm, with your thumb resting along the index and middle fingers. Turn fist toward the crowd.

Bucket

Candlestick

TIPS FROM THE COACH

Here's a way to make sure you're doing your candlesticks and buckets correctly. Clutch a straw! When you're doing your buckets, the ends of the straws should be perfectly parallel to the floor. When you do your candlesticks, the straws should be straight up and down (at a 90-degree angle to the floor).

Arm Movements

1. **High V:** Arms are raised in a high V position.

2. **Low V:** Arms are down and out to the side, forming an upside-down V.

3. **The T:** Arms are out to the sides straight from the shoulder, parallel to the ground.

4. **Half T:** Identical to the T, except that the arms are bent in at the elbow, with the hands in front of the shoulders.

5. ***The L:*** One arm is raised straight up in the air and the other arm extends out from the shoulder.

6. ***Touchdown:*** Raise both arms so that they appear to be straight up in the air. Your arms should be pressed close to your temples. (If you put your arms actually straight up, touching your ears, it will look as if your arms are behind you.)

7. ***Diagonal:*** One arm is up and the other is down so that the line of both arms makes a diagonal.

Leg Positions

1. ***Feet Together:*** Feet should be parallel to each other, an inch or less apart.

2. ***Feet Apart:*** Spread feet apart, about shoulder-width for the best balance.

3. ***Side Lunge:*** The lead leg is bent with the knee directly over the ankle, the back leg is straight out to the side, and the feet are perpendicular.

Side lunge

4. ***Front Lunge:*** One knee is forward and bent over the toes, while the other knee is straight and the leg is extended straight out behind you.

THE RIGHT APPROACH

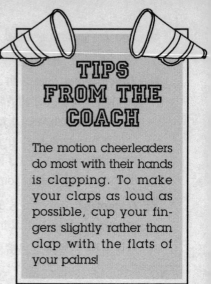

TIPS FROM THE COACH

The motion cheerleaders do most with their hands is clapping. To make your claps as loud as possible, cup your fingers slightly rather than clap with the flats of your palms!

Jumps are the most popular—and most impressive—cheerleading movement. They are fun to do and exciting to watch. Before you can execute a jump, you have to know how to start. The right approach will help you get the greatest height and the sharpest form in your jumps. You can use either of the following two approaches, depending on the one you feel most comfortable with.

★ ***Step Approach:*** Begin with both arms in a high V position. Take a step forward and swing both arms down, and then with another step bring both feet together. As you spring upward, lift your arms, legs, and head to gain maximum height.

★ ***Whip Approach:*** Start with arms in a V, but then, without stepping, swing both arms down and whip them back up as fast as you can, pushing down and then up with your legs to the desired position.

JUMP SKY-HIGH

Now the fun begins. A good jump is all a matter of timing, lift, and spring. Oh, and practice. Lots and lots of PRACTICE. Whatever jump you perform, make sure to keep your toes pointed, shoulders up, and head facing forward. When you land and rebound, always bend your knees slightly to absorb the shock.

1. **_Tuck:_** Bring knees to chest, making sure to keep your knees together.

2. **_Double Hook:_** Bend both legs to the same side, keeping knees facing forward.

3. **_Spread Eagle:_** Legs are straight out to either side, knees facing forward and toes pointed.

4. **_Herkie:_** One knee is bent and facing downward, while the other leg is fully extended to the side, parallel to the ground.

5. **_Side Hurdler:_** Kick your front leg to your chest and your back leg behind you. Your legs should be raised toward the sides, while your body should be facing front, toward the crowd.

6. **_Front Hurdler:_** Kick your front leg to your chest and bend your back leg behind you. Turn your body toward your front leg.

7. **_Toe Touch:_** Sit into the jump, extending both legs to the sides into a straddle position and bring your arms out. With chest up, touch hands with toes. (Now you know why you need to stretch those hamstrings!)

8. ***Double Nine:*** Kick forward and up with one leg and tuck the other leg in front of you, touching the opposite knee. (Your legs will look something like the numeral 9.) Hold your arms in a similar position.

8.

9. ***Pike:*** Keeping your legs together, raise your legs straight out in front of you, parallel to the floor. With your hands, reach for your toes.

9.

DOING IT TOGETHER

Partner stunts and pyramids are a dramatic addition to any cheer routine. At the high school level, pyramids and partner stunts are limited to two persons high. It's important to stay focused when working on the stunt—carelessness causes injuries. Basic skills must be perfected before you move on to more advanced stunts. Never attempt a stunt in front of a crowd before it is perfected. Every stunt and pyramid uses three basic positions:

★ ***Base:*** The bottom person who holds or lifts a partner.

★ ***Partner:*** The person on the second level of a stunt or pyramid who is held or lifted.

TIPS FROM THE COACH

With practice, you can attain maximum height in your jumps. This exercise might help: Use a sturdy box or step approximately 6 to 12 inches high. Place it on a mat. Using one of the two jump approaches, jump up onto the box ten times. Repeat this exercise two more times. As you feel more confident, increase the height of the box.

★ *Spotter:* The person who assists the base and partner until they've perfected the routine on their own. In more advanced stunts, the spotter stays in place throughout the stunt and assists in the dismount.

Partner Stunts

Also known as double stunts, partner stunts are when two or more cheerleaders perform together. Stunts can include climbing, lifting, and holding one of the partners. Here are a couple of the most popular stunts:

The Extension Prep

The Ground Up Liberty Stretch

Pyramids

Pyramids, which usually include a whole cheerleading team, are a combination of partner stunts that form a dramatic composition. A pyramid can be two layers high. Several bases form the bottom layer, and partners form the upper level. Here are a couple of the most popular pyramids:

The L Stand Pyramid

The Hitch Leg Pyramid

IN THE "SPOT"-LIGHT!

Safety first! That should be your motto every time you perform a partner stunt or pyramid. When you are learning a stunt, you should always have someone spot you. A spotter will help support your stunts until you feel confident enough to perform them safely on your own. The spotter's job is to help lift and steady you as you execute the stunt, and to assist on the dismount. The spotter may stand in front, back, or on either side and offer a steady hand and help break the fall if the stunt topples. Here are some tips to keep you safe.

Surroundings:

- Be sure to check the area where you are working for obstructions.
- Always work on level ground—mats or grass preferred. Avoid rocks, wet surfaces, concrete, and other dangerous materials or areas.
- Do not face the sun when attempting new partner stunts.

Attire/Accessories:

- Take off all jewelry.
- Avoid baggy shirts and shorts or shirts with pockets.
- Hair should be pulled back or worn in a ponytail. Avoid hard metal hair clips.

Hands-on Spotting:

- Always touch the stunt lightly with your fingertips if you can.
- Always spot the head and neck area first.
- Look at the stunt you are spotting.

THE ART OF YELLING

In leading a rowdy crowd, your voice is your most important means of communication. You need to learn how to use it and take care of it. If you don't, you risk getting a sore or raspy throat, or losing your voice altogether. How can you make your yells the best?

★ Always warm up your voice the way you warm up your other muscles. Begin by saying your cheers in a normal speaking voice. Gradually increase the volume until you are shouting in your best cheer yell!

★ Drive the sounds out from your diaphragm, not from your throat. Your diaphragm is a sheet of muscles separating your chest from the abdominal cavity.

★ Don't yell or scream in a high-pitched voice.

★ Articulate your words clearly and with the proper inflection.

★ Always avoid a dull, monotone voice.

CHEER OR CHANT?

Do you know a cheer from a chant? Or when to use each? Cheers are a form of entertainment designed to excite the audience. They are longer, and usually include stunts and pyramids. Chants are short supportive yells in which the crowd participates. Here are some general guidelines to keep in mind while cheering:

SECRET OF MY SUCCESS

"My vocal exercise to prepare for a cheer is to lie on my stomach, lift my feet up in the air (hold them there), put my hands on my stomach, and yell the words to my cheer. By holding your stomach you feel the words coming from there and not your throat."

KRISTI K.,
BARREN COUNTY HIGH SCHOOL,
GLASGOW, KENTUCKY

★ Cheers should be used at time-outs and at quarter breaks.

★ Cheers and chants should be functional and crowd-motivating. The purpose of cheers and chants is to get the crowd supporting your team, not for the cheerleaders to show off.

★ Someone needs to call "last time" or to step forward to designate when to stop the chant.

★ Football chants need to be performed when the teams are in their huddles, not when the actual play is happening.

★ Basketball chants are performed throughout the game except when a free throw is being shot. The game situation changes quickly in basketball, so cheerleaders must pay close attention.

THE THREE C'S: CAMPS, CLINICS, AND COMPETITIONS

The grueling tryouts are over and you've made it! Now there are three exciting activities you can look forward to doing with your squad: summer camps, year-round clinics, and competitions. Get psyched!

CAMPS

Every summer, thousands of cheerleaders head off for camp. However, these campers won't be hiking through the woods or weaving baskets made from pine needles. They will be learning the latest cheers and ways to improve their performances.

National cheerleading organizations generally sponsor the camps and gear them for cheerleaders who are already members of a squad. Most importantly, camp helps the squad to learn to work as a team. The cheerleaders solidify friendships that help build a squad's unity.

Camps are held during summer vacation for four or five days and are taught by trained instructors who have been cheerleaders themselves. Your school's cheerleading adviser will have information on upcoming camps and clinics. Here are a few types of programs to fit an individual squad's needs.

CHEER FOR THE DAY

Help to make the away team's squad feel welcome by introducing your squad to them just before the game or at halftime with this fun little cheer.

Hi, hello,
And how do you do?
The T.O. Lancers
Say hello to you!

Resident Camp

This is four days of intense workshops and learning with professionals. It's a sleep-away camp, usually held on a university or college campus in the summer. The cost of a four-day clinic can run between $150 to $200 per cheerleader. Many squads hold fundraising events throughout the year to help cover costs. These camps are usually open to spectators to watch the teams practice and compete.

Commuter Camp

With a curriculum similar to a resident camp, this three-day camp has the cheerleaders go home each night and return the next day. These camps usually run in the summer only and cost less than $100 per student.

One-Day Clinic

This extensive, one-day workshop may cover anything from cheerleading fundamentals to specific instruction on stunts and pyramids. These clinics run year-round and cost approximately $20 per cheerleader.

Youth Camp

This camp focuses on the basics of cheerleading for elementary school-aged youngsters. It is sometimes sponsored by a national organization, but more likely it will be put on by a local youth group or a high school cheerleading squad as a fund-raising event. The price of this event is $20 a day or less, depending on whether it's a one-day workshop or an extended program.

Specialized Camps

★ *Mascot Camp:* Classes are geared for mascots. Often this camp is run simultaneously with a regular cheerleading camp.

★ *Christian Camp:* This is a regular cheerleading camp in a Christian atmosphere that includes prayer meetings along with cheering.

★ *All-Star Camp:* An all-star camp is specifically for junior and senior all-star groups. Classes have been created to meet the needs of these squads. *(Read more about all-star squads on page 61.)*

The cost of these camps is about the same as for a resident camp. If your school or group can't attend one of the other types of camps, you can arrange for a private camp, where an instructor will come to your school for three days to teach curriculum tailored especially for your squad.

COMPETITIONS

A cheerleader's primary purpose is to encourage his or her school's teammates to beat the competition. But what about spirit leaders who want to create a little friendly competition among local cheer squads?

Almost all the national cheerleading organizations hold annual competitions, called *nationals,* which give cheerleaders a chance to show off their skills and compete against other cheerleaders. At competitions you'll see the best of the best, as squads perform advanced cheer routines, as well as partner stunts and pyramids. Squads can qualify to go to the nationals at summer camps and at regional competitions. Some organizations even allow squads to qualify by sending a videotape of their qualifying routines. The same judging criteria used at camps and regional competitions are used for the videotape applications.

Once a squad reaches nationals, they perform a cheer and receive points for various parts of their performance, rather than being judged against other squads. They are rated on the cheerleading fundamentals, including jumps, tumbling, and choreography.

Some state and regional athletic organizations hold cheerleading competitions during the school year, as do some colleges and universities. If you want more information about competitions, check with the cheerleading adviser.

BRING HOME A SPIRIT STICK

To some it's just a red, white, and blue wooden stick. To the cheerleading squad who wins it, it's a reward for their A-plus efforts. At NCA camps, the Spirit Stick is one of the awards given to motivate cheerleaders to develop team unity. There isn't any one thing that a squad must do to win a Spirit Stick. It might be given because a squad pulled together to help one of their members. Or it might be given because a squad helped another squad, not just their own members, learn a new cheer. The Spirit Stick stands for team unity and working together—genuine spirit!

The winning squads in these competitions receive first, second, and third place trophies. In some cases, gift certificates and scholarships are also given. Of course, as any cheerleader will tell you, it isn't bringing home a trophy that matters. It's striving to be your best. Also, while the actual competition routine may last only three or four minutes, the time a cheer squad invests in putting together a class act creates enough memories— heartwarming and hilarious—to *fill* a yearbook!

Competition Categories

Competitions are generally broken down into divisions, or categories. Though each organization has different criteria, they may include the following categories:

★ *Large Varsity:* Fifteen to twenty members at the high school level

★ *Medium Varsity:* Eleven to fourteen members at the high school level

★ *Small Varsity:* Ten members and under at the high school level

★ *Junior Varsity:* May have no seniors on the squad

★ *Junior High:* All squads made up of freshmen and younger, includes middle school and elementary ages

★ *Coed Varsity:* All squads with one or more males at the high school level, not including the mascot, who must be in full mascot costume

Other categories include the Best Partner Stunt Competition, Best Individual Cheerleader Competition, and Best Mascot Competition. (Mascots are judged for their animation, creativity, and use of props.)

A CHEERLEADER'S DIARY

So what would cheerleading camp really be like?
Sneak a peek at this page from one new cheerleader's diary.

Dear Diary:

I can't believe I'm finally at cheer camp. This is the second day and I'm amazed at all the stuff our squad has already done....

Cheerobics! Who'd believe an aerobics class could be so much fun—cheering and exercise together!

Our squad got a book filled with new cheers. We had some time to work on them during the day. Then tonight, we performed the cheers at evaluations. We won a Spirit Stick, too, for our squad's unity during the private coaching session. Isn't that great? About that private coaching—we learned a new partner stunt today, and Heather was my partner. I didn't think we could do it, but the instructor showed us how step-by-step!

Even dinner was fun! Got to eat with other cheering squads from across the state. It was cool because nobody was cliquey at all. Exchanged some ideas and phone numbers, too!

Buddy Time: Met with our buddy. That's the instructor the camp assigns to our squad. We spent some time talking about what we did today. He had some great suggestions on improving our performance. It's been lots of fun. I can't wait for tomorrow!

Cheery Night,
JEN

THE WINNING EDGE

What does it take to be a winner? Is it something so special that only a few people have it? Can it be learned? Or even copied? The first place to look for an answer is with a winner.

Making It onto a Winning College Squad

The Oklahoma State University cheerleaders know what it takes to be champions. The school's three squads (Varsity Coed Cheer, Poms, and All-Girl Cheer) have finished first in national competitions seven times and have been runners-up eight times in the last ten years.

While Oklahoma State's experience is unique, it doesn't mean making it onto other college cheerleading squads is a piece of cake. Competition is really stiff at the college level, award-winning squad or not. As many as fifteen to twenty people may be trying out for each spot. And most of those who are trying out were top cheerleaders on their high school squads.

To make the cut, college cheerleading hopefuls know they must perfect their skills while still in high school. If you're committed to making a college squad, you need to learn everything you can before trying out for the team. Write or call the adviser at the school for information on requirements for trying out. Some questions you may want to ask:

★ *How many squads are there and what types?*

★ *What are the eligibility requirements to try out?*

★ *What is the time commitment during the school year?*

★ *What's the financial commitment?*

★ *Are scholarships available?*

GET A SCHOLARSHIP FOR CHEERING

Almost two hundred colleges and universities offer scholarships or grants to cheerleaders. A scholarship might be just enough to cover textbook expenses, or it could be a full scholarship, as is offered at the University of Georgia and the University of Kentucky. Check with your cheerleading adviser or the athletic department of the college you're interested in attending to see if they award any partial or full scholarships for cheerleading. Here are a few more schools that offer some type of scholarship for cheerleading:

Oklahoma City University, Oklahoma City, Oklahoma

Pepperdine University, Malibu, California

Texas A&M, Kingsville, Texas

University of Alabama, Tuscaloosa, Birmingham, and Huntsville

University of Florida, Gainesville, Florida

University of Hawaii, Manoa, Hawaii

University of Minnesota, Minneapolis, Minnesota

University of Missouri, Columbia, Missouri

University of Nebraska, Kearney and Lincoln, Nebraska

Wichita State University, Wichita, Kansas

All-Star Squads

They're hot. And they're the latest craze! All-star cheer squads are not affiliated with a school but are sponsored by an independent organization. It may be a parks and recreation program or an organization set up just to sponsor a squad for competition. All-star squads hold tryouts and sometimes even search (college football coaches call it "scouting") for cheerleaders they think would make a great addition to the squad.

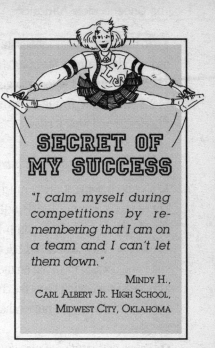

SECRET OF MY SUCCESS

"I calm myself during competitions by remembering that I am on a team and I can't let them down."

MINDY H.,
CARL ALBERT JR. HIGH SCHOOL,
MIDWEST CITY, OKLAHOMA

All-star squads perform in competitions and at special events, whether it's dazzling an audience at halftime festivities at one of the collegiate bowl games, or cheering in the original St. Patrick's Day Parade in Dublin, Ireland.

If an all-star squad appeals to you, check with your school adviser to see if there are any in your area.

MEET AMERICA'S #1 CHEERLEADER

The National Cheerleaders Association's "America's #1 Cheerleader" for 1995 was Liz Lorie. Liz attends Florida State University, maintains a 3.4 grade point average, and is a member of FSU's varsity cheerleading squad. In addition to winning a $10,000 educational scholarship from NCA, Liz has appeared on TV, had her photo run in *Teen* and *American Cheerleader* magazines, and was named one of the top collegiate cheerleaders in America by *College Sports* magazine. In the following interview, Liz talks about being a cheerleader and what it takes.

Q: How long have you been involved in cheerleading?

A: I've been doing it pretty much since I was seven or eight years old. There was a group of girls out on the playground and they were cheerleaders in the local youth league, the Palm Bay Youth Athletic Association. They were cheerleaders for the little football teams they had and I would watch them out on the playground. One day I went up to play with them, but I didn't know the cheers, so I had to sit out. They explained how I could join and try out for the team, and so the next year I tried out.

Q: From that youth league, did you go on to cheer on your junior high school cheering squad?

A: Actually, what happened was that the youth squad went all the way up to sophomores in high school. So rather than joining my middle school team, I decided to stay with the youth organization. It's what you'd call an all-star squad. So basically I started out on all-star teams and didn't join my school squad until my ninth-grade year. For a few years I was on two different squads—the high school team and the all-star squad.

Q: What activities prepared you for cheerleading?

A: First of all, I was really, really into gymnastics before I became a cheerleader. In cheerleading I found I could do my gymnastics, be in front of a crowd, and be a cheerleader. It was a lot of fun having teammates you performed with. I also had some dance in my background, ballet classes and tap.

Q: What is it like practicing on your college squad?

A: We usually have practice five days a week. Actually, I should say four. I say five because two hours before the game, we are supposed to be on the field, in uniform, practicing. So basically it's like having another practice right before we go cheer at a four-hour game.

Q: Do you do any additional workouts beyond your practice sessions?

A: During cheerleading season, I rarely work out aside from the practices because I feel the practices themselves give me everything I need for my stamina and my strength and keeping my weight down. The practices keep me in shape and help me stay strong. In addition to that, I try to watch what I eat. I eat things that are healthy and low in fat. But I'm normal, too—I do like chocolate! When I'm not cheering, I try to get to the gym to keep in shape.

Q: Do you have to try out for the squad each year?

A: Yes. A lot of people laugh when I say I'm nervous. But I know that if I don't go out and perform my absolute best, someone else could take my spot.

Q: Are there any jumps, movements, or stunts you have to work especially hard to master?

A: Yes, actually. When I was younger, it was my toe-touch jump. It was the really important jump to have—that's where both your legs are straight out. I remember I would go out to gymnastics and take a cheerleading-tumbling class, which is just floor gymnastics—no vault, bars, or beams. They would have a trampoline and I would get on it and jump and jump. Then I would get off the trampoline, and I'd go in front of the mirror and jump and jump.

Q: How has cheerleading helped you in the other parts of your life?

A: It's made such a big difference. In high school I ran for class president and I won. I really feel that if I hadn't had the confidence that cheerleading gave me, I wouldn't have had the courage to run. I think it's taught me discipline and dedication. It taught me how to get along with other people, and how to work in a team atmosphere. It really teaches you people skills that are important in life later on.

Q: What advice would you give to an aspiring cheerleader?

A: I would tell that person to really go at it 110 percent. I did because I really loved it and I still do. I think a lot of people who do things don't think that they could be the best, or that they could be one of the top people—but they can!

A CHEER-Y CAREER!

They don't touch a football or basketball, and yet they're the most famous women in the professional sports world today. "They" are the Dallas Cowboys Cheerleaders and the L.A. Laker Girls, who cheer on the Dallas Cowboys football team and the L.A. Lakers basketball players, respectively.

Almost all pro football and basketball teams use professional cheerleaders or dance squads to entertain during halftime. In this case, being a professional means you get paid to do what you do. Just like the cheerleaders in your school, professional cheerleaders have to try out every year. The biggest judging criterion is dancing ability. But while you might find some professional dancers on these squads, most of the members have other careers. Once they make the squad, they're required to perform at all the team's home games for that season. For their efforts, they receive a small paycheck and the opportunity to dance before thousands of people *and* be seen on national television.

BEYOND SCHOOL SPIRIT

Now that you know everything there is to know about what cheerleaders do on the sidelines (almost), here are some other responsibilities that are just as important that must get done behind the scenes.

FANTASTIC FUND-RAISING FUNDAMENTALS

It takes money to outfit a cheerleading squad. The average cost for uniforms and accessories varies widely and can easily add up to $300 per cheerleader. Then there are the extra expenses of travel, camps, and other supplies. Most schools can't cover the entire cost, and neither can the individual cheerleaders and their families. As a result, most squads hold fund-raising activities. Some squads have one big moneymaker a year, while others try to have several mini-events throughout the year. What's hot in bringing in that needed cash? Here are some unique ideas cheerleading squads have tried that have been successful.

Youth Clinics

This idea is becoming the number one fund-raising activity for squads. A youth clinic is a one-day cheerleading workshop for seven- to thirteen-year-olds. Members of the squad instruct youngsters on cheerleading basics. Price for the full-day event is about $20 per participant, but squads can charge more or less depending on where they live and the services provided. A youth clinic can be held at the school gym or a local recreation center. First, check with your school administration to find out if your school has the proper insurance to cover this kind of event. The squad adviser and a few parents are needed for supervision. The key to this fundraiser is advertising. Hang up signs in local elementary schools and pass out flyers to parents.

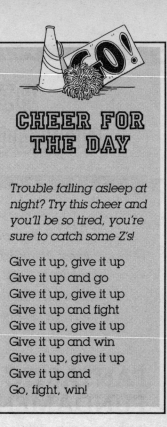

CHEER FOR THE DAY

Trouble falling asleep at night? Try this cheer and you'll be so tired, you're sure to catch some Z's!

Give it up, give it up
Give it up and go
Give it up, give it up
Give it up and fight
Give it up, give it up
Give it up and win
Give it up, give it up
Give it up and
Go, fight, win!

Dog Wash

Cars aren't the only things that get dirty! This is a great springtime fundraiser. Pick a location with lots of outdoor water faucets. Divide into two groups—washers and dryers. You'll also need someone to handle the money, as well as additional people to keep the waiting dogs in line. Promote your event with flyers, and make sure to post signs at veterinarians' offices. Charge about $5 per dog.

Game-A-Thon

You probably already know about telethons and walkathons—well, here's another kind of "thon"! Choose some games you love to play. Board games like Monopoly, Scrabble, Pictionary, and Trivial Pursuit are good because everyone is familiar with them. Jigsaw and crossword puzzles are fun, too. Like a walkathon, you need to get sponsors for each hour you play the games. Ask them to pledge fifty cents an hour, or more if they can. For this moneymaker to work, everyone on the squad has to be dedicated to getting sponsors.

The Cheer-Ful Haunted School

With your school's permission, turn a few classrooms and hallways into a Haunted School for Halloween after class hours. Dress up your monsters in cheerleader uniforms. Place a megaphone or pom pons in their paws and have them cheer (use a tape recorder or someone standing behind the scenes). Charge $3 to $5 for the Haunted School, and scare up some extra money by including a bake sale for those people waiting in line. For this activity to be a howling success, every squad member must be dedicated to creating the scariest, funniest haunt he or she can. As good advertising is also important, inform local elementary schools and youth organizations.

Balloons for the Heart

On Valentine's Day, people are always looking for something unique to give to that special someone. Why not provide balloon bouquets for your classmates? After getting permission from your school administrator, you'll need balloons (red, white, and pink for this holiday), a helium gas tank (check your Yellow Pages under "Gas" or "Helium"), and lots of ribbons. You might want to use a marker to write special messages on the balloons. If this fund-raising event goes well, think of providing balloon bouquets for other holidays. You'll probably be able to charge $2 a balloon, but make sure to figure in the cost of supplies before setting a price.

GET IN THE SPIRIT

The biggest challenge a cheerleader has is to build student body enthusiasm and promote school spirit, even when you're feeling under the weather or just having a bad day. One of the most effective ways you can positively influence the student body (and give you and your squad a lift as well) is with pep rallies. The best rallies create a feeling of unity among all the students, not just the athletes or upperclassmen. It's also a good way to create spirit for a special game, such as Homecoming or with the crosstown rivals. The more support your sports teams see, the harder they'll try on the field or court.

The pep club is sometimes responsible for putting together a pep rally. Cheerleaders, songleaders, baton twirlers, and other spirit groups in school make up the pep club. Early in the school year these groups get together to plan for the year. They'll decide how often to schedule the pep rallies and if there are any special events they would like to include.

The key to a successful pep rally is organization. Plan ahead and share responsibilities with the other members of the pep squad. Most pep rallies include the Pledge of Allegiance, cheers, the school song, and speeches from coaches, players, and the principal.

Planning a Rally That Rocks!

A pep rally is like any entertainment event. The same basic ideas are needed.

1. ***Grab the audience's attention.*** While students are walking to their seats, have the latest hot tune blasting over the loudspeaker. This will create an air of excitement before the cheerleaders even begin! Once everyone is seated, perform a splashy opening cheer.

2. ***Make 'em laugh.*** Laughter is a great way to get a message across. Use short, funny skits to make your

point, like football players dressed as cheerleaders to demonstrate a cheer.

3. ***Finish with a bang.*** Be sure to end the rally with the students feeling positive about their school. Have the coach or principal (preferably not in a cheerleading uniform!) lead everyone in a rowdy cheer.

Giving Extra PEP to Your Pep Rally

A little creativity will add that needed oomph! and POW! to an already awesome rally.

★ Often football players or other athletes will shave their heads or a strip of their heads to show unity during a season. Take advantage of their tradition and convince a few players to lose their hair at the rally!

★ Class competitions always bring out the rowdiness in a school. Separate the crowd into freshmen, sophomores, juniors, and seniors, and see who has the loudest spirit and the *most* class.

★ Pass out signs, balloons, banners, or little poms for kids to take to the game that afternoon or evening.

★ Have the pep rally some place other than the gym. Try a practice field, or hold an evening bonfire in a safe and well-supervised open area.

ON PEP RALLIES

"We like to do fun things so that the school doesn't get bored. We have funny songs and lots of crowd involvement. Our school really likes that."
——LEAH A., SHERANDO HIGH SCHOOL, STEPHENS CITY, VIRGINIA

"We usually give out Spirit Sticks. Sometimes they're the Spirit Sticks we got at NCA camp. Sometimes we make our own, like the giant one we did for Homecoming. We bought a long piece of PVC pipe and taped blue and gold stripes on it so it looked like a candy cane. We gave it to the class who showed the most spirit at the pep rally and they got to use it on their Homecoming float."
——WHITNEY W., MARATHON HIGH SCHOOL, MARATHON, FLORIDA

"We like to do dances for our pep rallies. Doing the latest dances gets everyone really pumped up."
——MERISSA B., BANNING HIGH SCHOOL, WILMINGTON, CALIFORNIA

THE DAILY "CHEER" REPORT

The image of a cheerleader performing in front of a crowd of roaring football fans has become part of our American culture. Some cheerleaders went on to become famous, and yet others, infamous! Several of these stories are so inspiring, they may give you something to cheer about. Other stories are so shocking, they'll give you something to talk about!

THE FAMOUS

Before they were famous—they were cheerleaders! When they were young, these stars graced football fields and basketball courts around the country. Now they're gracing stages and screens around the world!

★ **PAULA ABDUL** got a head start on her career as a singer (*Forever Your Girl, Head Over Heels*) and music video choreographer when she cheered for Van Nuys High School in Van Nuys, California, and later for the L.A. Lakers as a Laker Girl. It was on the Lakers court that she was discovered by Janet Jackson, who persuaded her to choreograph a video for her.

★ **HALLE BERRY** was a cheerleader before she came to the screen in such hits as *The Flintstones* and the TV miniseries *Queen*.

★ **SANDRA BULLOCK**, of *Speed, While You Were Sleeping,* and *The Net* fame, sure wasn't sleeping when she was cheering for Washington & Lee High School in Arlington, Virginia.

★ **KATIE COURIC**, the early-morning riser and host of the *Today* show, cheered for Yorktown High School in Arlington, Virginia.

★ **SALLY FIELD**, Emmy- and two-time Oscar-winning actress for *Norma Rae* and *Places in the Heart* (and who also starred in megahit *Forrest Gump*), could be found cheering for her team at Birmingham High School in Van Nuys, California.

EXPOSED—LUKE PERRY— A FREDDIE BIRD!

Luke Perry, that handsome hunk from television's *Beverly Hills 90210,* spent part of his high school career under feathers. Luke was the school mascot, Freddie Bird, at Fredericktown High School in Fredericktown, Ohio. For one game, he arranged for a helicopter to land on the field, from which he emerged dressed in yellow tights, red plumes, a cape, and giant webbed feet!

★ **SUSAN LUCCI** was jumping for joy on the Garden City High School cheerleading squad in New York before she became the star of the popular soap opera *All My Children.*

★ **MADONNA**, recording artist of such megahits as "Material Girl" and actress in *Desperately Seeking Susan,* honed her entertaining skills while cheering at Adams High School in Rochester, Michigan.

★ **ANN-MARGRET** cheered for New Trier Township High School in Winnetka, Illinois, and went on to star in movies with such Hollywood leading men as Elvis Presley, Jack Nicholson, and *Grumpy Old Men* co-stars Walter Matthau and Jack Lemmon.

★ **STEVE MARTIN**, comic actor and "crazy guy," starred in *Parenthood* and *Father of the Bride,* and cheered on the Garden Grove High School football team in Southern California.

★ **MERYL STREEP**, two-time Oscar-winning actress for *Kramer vs. Kramer* and *Sophie's Choice* (and also the star of *The River Wild* and the romantic *The Bridges of Madison County*), was a cheerleader at Bernardsville High School in New Jersey.

★ **NIKI TAYLOR** may be a Cover Girl supermodel now, but when she was five years old she was cheering for the North Dade Optimist Football League in Miami, Florida.

★ **VANNA WHITE**, hostess of the TV game show *Wheel of Fortune,* cheered at North Myrtle Beach High School in South Carolina.

NEVER TOO OLD

Who are the oldest cheerleaders in the United States? The Sun City Pom Poms in Arizona. Their average age is seventy-three years young, and they're always ready to perform their routines at retirement homes, schools, and even on television!

THE INFAMOUS

Every once in a while a story comes around that tickles your funny bone or leaves you shaking your head in disbelief. Here are three stories about cheerleaders that are sure to do the same.

The Obsessed Mother

Wanda Holloway is one mother who took cheerleading way too seriously. She was determined that her daughter, Shanna Harper, would make the cheerleading squad at Channelview High School in Texas.

To Wanda, it seemed that her daughter was always coming in second best to Amber Heath. Shanna, Wanda's daughter, was talented, but she was edged out at each tryout by Amber. This must have seemed so unfair to Wanda, who had always wanted to be a cheerleader when she was in high school. Now she wanted the same dream for her daughter.

On September 3, 1991, Wanda was convicted of trying to hire a hit man to kill the mother of her daughter's cheerleading rival. The prosecution's star witness against Wanda was her former brother-in-law, Terry Harper. He said Wanda believed Amber would be so upset over her mother's death that she would drop out of cheerleading tryouts. Wanda was ready to give him a pair of diamond earrings to pay for a hit man. The jury must have believed him, because Wanda was found guilty and sentenced to fifteen years in prison. Currently, a new trial has been granted for Wanda because of a problem with one of the jurors in the first trial. Wanda has also agreed to pay Verna Heath, the intended target, $150,000 to settle a civil suit.

Who Was That Girl?

At first glance there wasn't anything extraordinary about Cheyen Weatherly. She was just a seventeen-year-old new transfer who made the cheerleading squad at Coronado High in Colorado

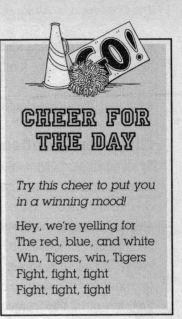

Springs, Colorado, in the fall of 1990. But there was something very, very different about Cheyen.

For starters, Cheyen had an exotic background. She'd lived in Greece and had been privately tutored for her first two years of high school.

Then, there was her size. At 5' 9" and 164 pounds, she was the largest member of the cheerleading squad. That didn't seem to bother any of the cheerleaders, as her size made her a strong base for the human pyramid.

And, of course, there was that five o'clock shadow that set this blue-eyed brunette apart from the other cheerleaders! When school officials discovered that Cheyen's transcripts were phony, they called the police to investigate. That's when they discovered that seventeen-year-old Cheyen Weatherly was really twenty-six-year-old Charles Daugherty, a female impersonator with a record of arrest for burglary and theft.

Daugherty has since appeared on the Sally Jessy Raphael talk show, claiming that Cheyen was just one of his five multiple personalities. In an earlier incident, he turned up as Shannon Ireland Trump and won a spot on the cheerleading squad of the Colorado Springs Spirit, a now-defunct minor league football team. No one knows why Charles Daugherty did what he did. Was it one of his many "personalities" driving him to be a cheerleader? Or was it just a desire for recognition?

Chips for Cheerleading

By all accounts, it's an unusual fund-raising activity, one that most cheerleading squads would not want to attempt. In 1987, the Clayton High cheerleaders in Clayton, New Mexico, needed to raise some money in order to travel to the state basketball tournament in Albuquerque. So the team enlisted the help of Betsy, a 1,500-pound Holstein cow whose contribution to the fund-raising event was, well, a cow patty!

In this farming community, cow patties are a common sight and smell. So naturally, someone came up with an idea to use them for a fund-raising event.

The kids on the squad marked off 162 squares on the school's football field. The squares were raffled for $10 apiece. Or a whole row of nine squares could be bought for a mere $40. Whoever owned the square where Betsy deposited her contribution would win $500.

On the windy, 30-degree day, two hundred people gathered to watch Betsy. She wasn't too cooperative. She wandered around the football field for more than two hours. The crowd got restless and left. There were only ten spectators still watching when Betsy finally dropped her patty.

It was a happy ending for all. The Clayton High cheerleading squad raised $1,300 and went on to root their team on to a win in the championship game. And Betsy was just relieved, literally!

JUST ONE OF THE BOYS: AN INTERVIEW WITH A MALE CHEERLEADER

He may not be famous—or infamous—but John Gillis does have something that sets him apart from 96 percent of the cheerleaders in America. He's a guy! John attends the University of Texas at Austin. He's a senior and a psychology major and has been on the cheer squad for three and a half years. Read on for a guy's-eye view from the sidelines.

Q: What made you try out for the cheer squad in high school?

A: I was a football player. There were two guys on the cheer squad and one was graduating. One day my Latin teacher asked if there were any guys who were interested in trying out. Cheerleading appealed to me as another activity to replace football. And it was a challenge to do something new.

Q: Did you have any gymnastic skills?

A: I had no gymnastic skills. None! The only thing I had to learn was a standing flip-flop for that tryout. A month or two before tryouts, I just went to private lessons and group lessons over and over again.

Q: What got you through that very first tryout?

A: I think it was the most adrenaline I've ever had in my entire life. After the tryout, I just kept running around the gym for a couple of minutes doing jumps and yelling for the crowd. Their reaction to me had gotten me through that tryout. But that's also what's kept me in cheerleading for so long. Just seeing a crowd's reaction to what you're doing makes your job all worthwhile, and that's the fun of being a cheerleader.

Q: *You were one of two guys on your high school squad. How about your college squad?*

A: It's fifty-fifty here. There are seven couples on the squad.

Q: *What is the difference between high school cheering and college cheering?*

A: Stunts take over in college and jumps become less important. But the main thing in both high school and college cheering is trying to emphasize crowd response. That's your primary goal. Jumps, tumbling, stunts, and pyramids are all aimed at getting the crowd to respond.

Q: *What do you enjoy doing the most?*

A: Stunting is fun. It's almost new every year because the stunts change and get harder and harder. I think any guy is happy once he learns an "awesome." That's holding both feet of a girl with one hand.

Q: *With school, practice, and games, do you have a social life?*

A: I really try to. I'm in school for studies first. When you have time commitments, like cheerleading or any other organization, you need to be able to study whenever you can. That means you come home in the afternoons and study. Cut down, or out, your TV and play time. So you get your studying done, then your cheerleading, and use whatever time you have left to play.

ONE LAST HURRAH!

It takes a special person to be a cheerleader. Ask yourself this: Are you willing to give up a lot of time and energy to practice? Can you juggle the responsibilities of school, home, and cheering? Are you someone who goes out of your way to promote school spirit? Do you have a whole lot of enthusiasm to spare? Are you READY?. . .OKAY—GO FOR IT!

Check out the magazine! It's not affiliated with any national organization. Write to them for a subscription, or look for it on your newsstand.

**American Cheerleader
Lifestyle Publications
350 W. 50th St., Suite 2AA
New York, NY 10019**

INDEX

★ ★ ★ ★ ★